BOTTLING BURPS FOR GRANDMA

CSO

BOTTLING BURPS
FOR GRANDMA

by

Andrew Collett

Illustrated by Debbie Hookway

The King's England Press
1999

ISBN 1 872438 27 X

Bottling Burps for Grandma is typeset by Moose Manuscripts
in Garamond 12pt and published by
The King's England Press Ltd,
21, Commercial Road, Goldthorpe,
Rotherham, South Yorkshire, S63 9BL

Printed and bound in Great Britain by

Woolnough Bookbinding
Irthlingborough
Northamptonshire

FOREWORD

A very BIG thank you!

Big people, small folk, young and old, mothers, grandads and many more of you around the country have been buying-up large quantities of my previous collection of rotten rhymes, *Always Eat Your Bogies*. Children and adults alike seem equally enthusiastic to read about everlasting nappies and cow pats with pet names. So, thank you!

But what does this all say about the great British buying public? Could it be that we all have an undying fascination with rancid and rotten things? Or could the answer be much simpler? Could the appeal of books such as *Always Eat Your Bogies* be much easier to explain - is it simply be that everyone likes to laugh?

As in the case of *Always Eat Your Bogies* this second collection does not aim to fit in with any one 'type' of poetry. Its objective, pure and simple, is to present reading as something which is fun. Hopefully, it's a message which might stick.

Happy reading! Kind Regards,

Andrew Collett

Dedications

To my wonderful son, Toby, for understanding when I'm too busy to play pea-shooters with the vacuum cleaner in the kitchen. Thanks Toby!

To my equally wonderful and long-suffering wife for living me and my very strange habits. Oh, - and for picking those peas off the kitchen floor!

Bottle Your Burps For Granny!

Bottle your burps
keep them as new,
save them for later
store them in goo!

Let them grow old
let them grow mean,
let your big burps
turn nasty and green.

Watch as they rot
wait as they worm
watch their wild faces
starting to squirm.

Then when they're ready
then when they're done
be ready to have
some big-burping fun!

Just loosen the lid
and leave in the shade,
stick on a label -
call it marmalade.

Then wait for your granny
to call round for tea,
hide in a corner,
count up to three!

Sit really still
watch from afar,
as your old granny
opens that jar.

Then cover your ears
wait for the sound,
of an ear-bursting burp
rocking the ground.

And as it comes
stay in your place,
as one giant burp
lands in her face.

Slipping and sliding
in green bits of goo,
frothing and foaming
like dead bits of stew.

But don't be amazed
if she then tries for a taste,
for grannies won't ever
let food go to waste!

Recycle That Nappy!

Don't throw away that nappy
don't drop it in the bin,
for with a dirty nappy
you can do anything!

It could be a pair of earmuffs
for Grandad when he's cold -
he wouldn't notice the smell
now he's growing old.

It could be a duster
to wax and shine in one,
leaving all your furniture
with a special kind of pong.

It could be a teddy
to cuddle through the night,
turning all your sheets
to a funny shade of white.

It could be some candy floss
if you coloured it in pink,
and it would make a deadly weapon
with that rather lovely stink.

So don't throw away that nappy
don't drop it in the bin,
for, with a dirty nappy,
you can do anything!

9

Sir Arnold De-Sacks

Sir Arnold De-Sacks
could pour out earwax
wherever he happened to be,
he could be reading a book
or taking a look
at something right out to sea.

But still it would ooze from his ear
running quite clear,
it would gush like gravy on tap,
with a roar and a rush,
some dribble, some mush,
it would slosh all over his lap.

Which is the reason
last earwax season,
Arnold did everything right,
for when it started to drop
he just licked it all up
for Arnold has quite an appetite!

The Earwax Worm

The hair in Dad's ear
grows by the day,
squeezing out earwax
which gets in its way.

It's like a small creature
feeding on goo,
worming and wriggling
then starting to chew.

Sucking and spitting,
sliding about,
as this tiny creature
tries to get out.

Munching and crunching
earwax and slime,
as it twists and it turns
in an ear full of grime.

Then with a push,
one great big pop,
the creature comes out
covered in slop.

Which is the moment
we start to be sick,
and Dad starts to laugh
at his great party trick.

Do Head Lice Do Handstands?

Do head lice do handstands
when sat on your head?
Do they play games
as they wait to be fed?

Do they run riot
and party all day,
drinking bottles of blood
all served on a tray?

Do they have outings
down to your toe?
Do they play hide-and-seek
as hair starts to grow?

Do they watch telly
with such a good view?
Do they read the paper,
just like me and you?

Do head lice do handstands?
Do they all like to play?
For it must be quite boring
stuck up there all day!

The Sleeve

You can sneeze on it
and wheeze on it,
you can drip on it
and be sick on it.

You can spill on it
and be ill on it,
but this isn't quite
the very best bit!

For no matter what you do with it
it always comes up new with it,
so come on everyone have a heave
and celebrate the trusty sleeve!

My Grandad's Bad Breath

My grandad's bad breath
is sweeter than sweet,
it has the whiff
of cheesy green feet.

It has the pong
of old underwear,
it has the stench
of mouldy
old hair.

My grandad's breath
is so very bad,
for he's not cleaned his teeth
since he was a lad.

14

Nibble A Nose

Nibble a nose
take a small bite,
chew it and chomp it
all day and night.

Nibble a nose
one bit at a time,
crunch at the crust
or slurp at the slime.

Nibble a nose
don't even think twice,
for nibbling noses
is really quite nice.

Nibble a nose
start with a friend,
start a new fashion,
start a new trend.

Nibble a nose,
one big and one small,
for nibbling noses
is good for us all!

Everyone's Eating Bogies

Everyone's eating bogies
right across the town
old ladies and small babies
can't wait to gulp them down.

Some chew them really quickly
as they dribble on their clothes,
some keep them all for later
putting them back inside their nose.

Some make them fresh and fluffy
by bottling them in twos,
some like to let them season
in the soles of both their shoes.

Some fry and bake and boil them
some pile them up on toast,
some think they're good with honey,
others grill them on a roast!

Some suck them really slowly
like an old boiled sweet,
some gulp them down in mouthfuls
as if they hadn't had much to eat.

For everyone's eating bogies
right across the town,
for once that you have started
you just can't put them down!

Brian's Bendy Backside

Brian's bendy backside
was so difficult to hide,
it just bounced and bopped every day.

For a bendy bum
is never much fun
for it always gets in the way.

It liked to pop out
and wobble about,
it liked to pull funny faces.

With a little cough
it would start to show off
when visiting all kinds of places.

It once blew a kiss
with a deadly hiss
when visiting the vicar for tea.

He ran for cover
but was soon to discover
there's no escape from a bottom that's free!

It once dealt a blow
to a lady I know
who wanted to keep it as a pet.

It sorted her in one
with another awful pong -
something she'll never forget!

For this bottom's not dim,
although not at all thin,
it does almost everything well.

But what is does best,
as you've probably guessed,
is to make the most horrible smell!

Before The National Health Service

In Victorian days
there was no NHS,
so surgeons didn't mind
if they made a mess.

They found it exciting
just messing about,
deep down in your innards
and pulling things out.

It was all very new,
not done before,
yanking and throwing
your bits to the floor.

And what made it special
is that people would queue
to watch and discover
the real inner you.

So that's how it was,
a bit of a mess,
back with the Victorians
before the NHS.

Sneezes

When you start to cough
your mouth fills with froth
where once your food had been,
before exploding in one
like an enormous great bomb
and showering the world with
green.

Always Eat Your Bogies 2

Always eat your bogies
that's how the poem goes,
chew and crunch and munch them
as they wriggle out your nose.

Always eat your bogies
it's a poem set in slime,
do you always eat your bogies?
I know that I eat mine!

Always eat your bogies
don't hesitate to think,
just always keep some fresh
in the bottom of your sink.

Always eat your bogies
eat one then two then three,
but please always remember
to save the last for me!

Dinosaur Talk

'Mum! Mum! There's a dinosaur on the telly!'

That's nice dear. I do like it when you watch educational programmes.'

'But Mum! There's a dinosaur on the telly!'

Well you just enjoy watching it then.'

'But Mum, there's ......'

CRASH! BANG! CRASH!

What's that dear?'

Grip Your Granny By Her Girdle

Grip your granny by her girdle
spin her round and round,
watch those false teeth start to shake
as she rises off the ground.

Pull her petticoat into line
don't let those bloomers burst,
then spin her even faster,
go on - do your worst!

But watch out for crashing curlers
don't let them do you in,
just enjoy watching Grandma
as she gets into a spin.

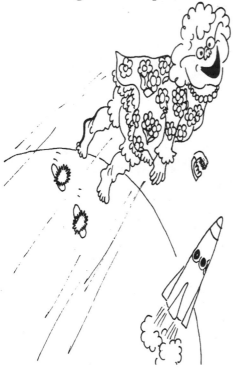

Then when she's going fast
and all red in the face,
let go of her girdle
as she shoots to outer space.

But don't you stop to worry
as she flies across the town,
for you know that what goes up
must also come back down!

Chew Chew Chew

Dad chews his meat
when we're at tea,
then spits it out
to share with me.

He says it's best
to suck the skin,
he says it keeps
the vitamins in.

But what gets me
about Dad and food,
is that the meat
is only half-chewed.

Which is the reason
I open my jaw
to chew and chew
the meat some more.

I gnaw and nibble
I suck it whole,
before spitting it back
into the bowl.

So, at last,
we can tuck-in
to chewed-up meat
with vitamins in!

False teeth are the fashion

False Teeth are the fashion
just throw those jewels away,
for you'll look good in false teeth
at any time of day.

Old ladies of distinction
wear them all with pride
they dangle from their ears
and swing from side to side

Movie stars across the world
have false teeth in their hair
and its said that pop starts
put them in their underwear!

For false teeth are the fashion
so throw those jewels away,
for you'll look good in false teeth
at any time of day

Let's Buy A New Bottom

If your backside's gone grey
if your backside's gone rotten
then why don't you nip out
to buy a new bottom?

There must be a place
where these things are done,
there must be a place
to buy a new bum!

One without pimples
and wriggly round hair,
one which looked nice
even when bare.

One which would fit
into any kind of clothes,
one which behaved
should you come to blows!

One without wobble
one with real style,
one completely without
that big-bottom smile.

One which was comfy
one which was slim,
one which was borrowed
from someone quite thin.

For there must be a place
where these things are done,
there must be a place
to buy a new bum!

Wet Nonsense

When it's raining
down in the sea
do whales have wipers
so they can see?

Do squids have lids
to keep them dry?
And do lobsters hold
umbrellas high?

Do dolphins dance
in puddles wide?
Do jellyfish race
to get inside?

Do king prawns cover
their golden crown?
And do sea cows really
all lie down?

Teachers' Tummy Buttons

In teachers' tummy buttons
you won't find much that's nice,
except old bits of tummy fluff
and tiny chocolate mice.

You'll find some lumpy custard
and broken bits of chalk,
you'll find some rhubarb crumble
and a dirty knife and fork.

You'll find an old jam sandwich
and a toffee still half-chewed,
for, deep down in tummy buttons,
is where teachers keep their food!

The Disadvantages of A Reversible Rear

Let us be clear
about a reversible rear,
it's not everything that you might think.

For, if not thinking right,
you could have a fright
and face the most terrible stink.

For, a reversible rear
could cost you dear
if, for a moment, you should ever doze.

For with one wild flip
your bottom could slip
and stick itself into your nose!

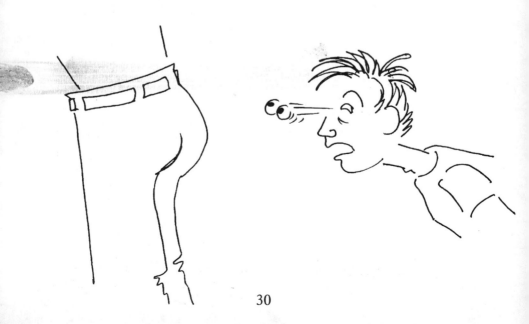

One Rule For Me!

I once broke a window
and got in real trouble,
I once lost my homework
so Dad gave me double.

I once flooded the hall
and had to clean up the floor,
and Mum fed me soap
when she heard that I'd swore.

So why is it my sister
is never sent to bed,
if she shouts at my dad
or paints her room red?

Why is it my sister
always gets off scot-free?
Is there one rule for her
and one rule for me?

The Worst Class's Promise

(To be chanted every morning)

We promise not to do our homework
and never to try our best,
we promise to always pull wild faces
and cheat in every test.

We promise to be late every morning
and spoil everybody's fun,
we promise to talk in class
and to never walk, but run!

We promise to do all these things
we promise to break every rule,
for we promise you that we
are the worst class in our school!

Putrid Pizzas

Have you ever wondered
where bogies go when dead?
What happens to your dandruff
when it's finished on your head?

Well the answer to these questions,
the answer to this tale,
is that they're gathered in
and then put up for sale.

Before being bought by restaurants
and supermarkets everywhere,
to be used as pizza toppings
for everyone to share.

So if you ever walk
through a pizza parlour door,
don't be surprised if you've
seen their toppings once before!

Show-Off

You always show-off
you don't seem to care,
you'll do anything
just for a dare!

You make others laugh
you make them join in
with your wink of an eye
and wide-eyed great grin.

But when we're alone
with no one around,
you just sit in the corner,
you don't make a sound.

When there's just me
you don't even try,
there's no grin on your face
or wink in your eye.

But that's when you're real,
that's when you're true,
two friends together -
that's when you're you!

Knight Relief

Way way back many years ago
jousting was the thing,
with knights riding on grand horses
with a pole long and thin.

And the reason for such nonsense,
the reason this was done,
wasn't to give all the onlookers
some really gory fun!

The answer was much simpler
for the logic to such acts
was so that poor old knights
could have a proper scratch.

For with all that armour
and all those weighty clothes,
they could not scratch their back
or even tickle at their toes.

Which is why it was so splendid
watching knights get in a pickle,
running round with long poles
to give each other a tickle.

It really was quite a sight
as they ran with one pole each,
just to give each other a tickle
in the parts they couldn't reach.

Ten Foot Terry

Ten-foot Terry is never lost
for friends when out all day,
with one look from his giant face
everyone agrees to play.

For no one dares to argue
with Terry at their side,
for he's over ten foot tall
and nearly just as wide.

Teachers all play tiddlywinks
with Terry after school,
giving him ten team points
each time he plays the fool.

Old ladies kick off curlers
to play football in the park,
and great big growling dogs
ask before they bark.

The Prime Minister and the President
always invite him round for tea,
and if he wants to see the Queen
then Terry has a key.

For everyone's friends with Terry
everyone tries their best,
for no one wants him in a temper
as I'm sure you've probably guessed!

Toga Toga

The Romans ruled with courage
the Romans ruled with passion,
but the poor old Romans
never ruled with fashion.

For they weren't very trendy
they weren't very sleek,
wandering round the country
in nothing but a sheet.

Perhaps they thought it clever
perhaps they thought it wise,
perhaps the poor old Romans
thought it such a good disguise.

Perhaps they thought it hip
perhaps they thought it groovy,
perhaps they'd seen it done before
when watching some old movie.

But whatever their reason
there was little justification
for running round in bed clothes
when such a powerful nation.

So I wonder if they'd worn
something more sensible instead,
then the great Roman Empire
might not have wound up dead.

Colonel Reginald Blow-Him-Up Dan

Colonel Reginald Blow-Him-Up Dan
liked to plant bombs in the lavatory pan,
he squashed them in tight, two at a time,
connecting them all to an old washing line.

At first he began with Dame Lady Potter
not much of a lady, a bit of a rotter,
and waiting for her to take load off her feet
he tugged only once on the old toilet seat.

But there was not heard a bang, a breaking of bottom,
of poor Dame Potter particularly rotten
only a stretch, a creak as the line pulled tight
and she tucked in her bloomers well out of sight.

He pulled it again, a little more force,
Dame Potter, by now, should have exploded of course
he pulled for the last time, it was all very wrong,
then bouncing it came - the line and one bomb!

And came the other, following up the rear,
wobbling across, particularly near,
to where Dan sat shaking, wobbling with fright,
two bombs on target - climbing in height.

Dan dived into sink and covered his eyes
with bomb number one gaining in size,
he let out a scream, then stuck out his tongue,
sucked at his finger and shouted, 'Oh Mum!'

Dame Lady Potter, on hearing this howl,
pulled her worst face, incredibly foul,
the one where her whiskers wriggle on her chin
and her glass eye pops out and into the bin.

Then two bombs both hovered, not blowing to bits,
but pausing to ponder and count up to six
for, though right on target, at Dan and the sink
they needed a moment, a minute to think.

Time to consider, to plan what to do,
now that the targets had doubled to two:
one Reginald Dan, beginning to cry,
and Dame Lady Potter, all whiskers - no eye!

Then in a flash, without any sign,
bomb number one shouted, 'She's mine!'
But, not before number two had started to cough -
a signal to tell the other to keep off!

But number one bomb, though not very old,
had lived long enough not to do as he's told,
he let out a growl and poked at his middle,
number two poked back and they started to giggle.

And then it began, no one could stop,
it was perfectly ridiculous, quite over the top,
one pair of bombs wiping their eyes,
tickling each other and slapping their sides.

Then taking his chance, Dan ran for the door,
past giggling bombs, both sat on the floor,
for there's two things to do when bombs start to play:
run straight for cover and keep out their way!

But number one bomb, knowing this game,
decided to stop and quickly took aim
twisting around and counting to two
he fired at Dame Potter, still sat on the loo.

Waggling her toes, scratching that chin,
stretching her bloomers down to the bin
fishing one eye out she shouted, 'If fits!'
Just as bloomers and bottom were blown into bits.

'What a great shot!' giggled Dan, keeping low,
forgetting completely one bomb still to go,
and taking his time he opened the door
as one eye bounced over, across the floor.

All green and slimy, wobbling about,
blocking his exit - the only way out!
For even in toilets with doors set to spare
of ways in and out there's rarely a pair.

Dan started to growl, ready to shout,
at glass eye down below, rolling about,
he'd teach it a lesson, one not to forget,
he'd sort it out without any sweat.

And twisting around, he stuck out his chest,
lifted one foot to put to the test
to have some fun, a bit of a hoot -
squashing one eye into his boot.

'Not quite so fast,' came a hum from below,
rolling once over, ever so slow,
'we've not finished yet,' grinned back number two,
flicking the eye from under Dan's shoe.

Dan froze, he stopped with foot in the air,
above bomb number two, last of a pair,
knowing one wiggle, a slip of his toe,
would blow him to pieces - as you probably know!

And breathing in deep, biting his lip,
with no one to help, he needed a tip,
one bomb-beating plan, a bit of a clue
of how to escape - just what he could do.

So keeping foot still, trying to grin,
he had an idea to save his skin,
he'd be as brave as he could - a real man of steel,
and talk to the bomb - strike up a deal.

And bending right down, as if out of the blue,
'My dear chap,' he began, 'how do you do?
You see, old boy, if you could step over here,
I've something to say - a word in your ear.'

'Delighted, what fun, if you're really quite sure,'
replied number two, turning once more,
'but, dear chap, if it's the same to you
I'll stay where I am, under your shoe!'

Still trying to smile Dan said, 'Let's call it quits,
take all you want, just don't blow me to bits.
I'll give you riches, gold and what's more -
for a bomb I can tell you you'll never be poor!'

When suddenly from behind, just up the rear,
came someone else, ever so near,
a whiskery chin, an eye that's no more,
bloomers all blown up, bottom quite sore!

BOMB

Looking quite mad, her undies in threes,
one bit on the floor, two bits round her knees,
feeling and looking awfully funny,
but ready to give Dan a run for his money.

Ready to pounce, do Reginald in,
she whipped from her bloomers something quite thin,
a weapon so deadly, no one would think,
it could kill at ten paces - one duster, all pink.

The bomb sat still, not turning with speed,
knowing that soon the terrible deed
of flipping his lid, starting to blow,
would be over as soon as duster hit toe.

But if you're wondering how feather and stick
could do someone in - perform such a trick,
it's as easy as pie, two pieces of cake,
with one duster, all pink, and long as a rake.

Just search out a target, toe in the air,
foot number two, last of a pair,
and if underneath, all shiny and black,
you see one small bomb, the rule is attack!

Dame Potter took aim, starting to grin,
shouting out loud from whiskery chin,
and tickling her target right in his middle
one Reginald Dan started to giggle.

The duster, all pink, long as a rake,
turned twice on his tummy, starting to shake,
sending poor Dan screeching, 'Please, oh no more!'
and one foot in the air, crashing to the floor.

Crunching the bomb, squashing it tight,
one little black body hidden from sight,
but not blowing to bits, or starting to shoot,
just sat there, all smiling, under Dan's boot.

Dame Potter dropped her duster, eye turning red,
a growl from her chin, smoke from her head,
which is probably the same as anyone would do,
if blown up by a bomb when sat on the loo.

'Birdbrain! Bomb bandit! It's all been a fix!
You'd diddle your granny with one of your tricks!
You should have been blown up, bits in the air!'
Cried out Lady Potter screaming, 'Not fair!'

Dan smiled, still shaking, feeling quite lame,
one eye on the bomb, two on the dame,
she moved towards him, looking quite mean,
as the smoke from her ears now turned to steam.

'Please, don't come any closer,' cried Reginald Dan,
'get out of the room, escape while you can!
Scarper, get lost, unless you're bomb-proof,
one wiggle of my foot and we'll both hit the roof.

'Oh no, not likely, me little old fruit,
it's you, not me, who's going to scoot,
out of the bathroom and into the hall,
I'm going to play rugby - with you as the ball!'

'Rugby!' giggled Dan, a wiggle of toe,
watching her bloomers hanging down low,
you couldn't play tiddlywinks with those round your knees,
unless you tied them up in knots and tried not to sneeze.

Dame Potter turned white, her one eye all green
both of her ears still churning out steam,
and with flick of her wrist, a gritting of teeth
she whipped off her bloomers from down underneath.

Spinning them round, ready to fight,
they twisted and turned, gaining in height,
up to her whiskers, past eye that's no more,
as she started to count, slowly to four.

One and a two - they started to swing!
Three - their elastic snapped with a ping!
Four - a rip, a shred and a tear
as bloomers, all twisted, flew through the air.

'Brilliant!' clapped Dan, 'a great party trick!'
not hearing at all the quiet tick tick,
or spotting above him, bloomers unmanned -
H.M.S. Undies preparing to land!

48

Hovering up high, a real birdseye view,
of Reginald Dan and one blasted-up loo,
not moving a muscle, but keeping quite still,
ready to pounce - go in for the kill!

'See, you couldn't play rugby, not in that frock!'
Dan shouted as the bomb whispered tick tock,
'I told you to play tiddlywinks or ludo instead!'
Dan giggled and H.M.S. Undies dive-bombed his head.

'Oh no!' he cried, 'you've put out the light!'
'I know,' said Dame Potter, ready to fight,
'you see, when I play rugby with you as the ball,
it's much more fun when you can't see at all.'

And not waiting to say pardon or get ready to fight
Dame Potter arm-wrestled his ear, squashing it tight,
tugging him forwards, lifting up high,
as Dan shot through the ceiling and into the sky.

Then in less than it took to say bloomers are best,
the bomb jumped in the air and banged on its chest,
chasing Dan skywards, target in sight,
as it flew through the air, increasing in height.

'Oh!' cried Dame Potter, full of surprise,
hardly daring to believe her eyes
the one on her face by the eye that's no more
and another, all glass, sat on the floor.

Rolling and turning, following the race,
between Dan and the bomb, shooting through space,
one in the lead, bomb on his tail,
all going to plan - now nothing could fail.

'Get him!' shouted Dame Potter, at roof and one hole.
'Blow him to pieces, make his head roll!
Bulldoze his backside, put a flea in his ear,
that'll sort him for good, and keep him well clear!'

She waved as Reginald climbed up in height
before disappearing for good - right out of sight,
then walking right over to blown-up seat
she sat down on her bottom, took load off her feet.

But as she sat there, with feet on the ground,
she was blown to pieces in a bomb-blasting sound,
for she should remember that, in any town,
what goes up must also come down.

And so let this be a lesson, if ever alone,
and sat on the seat with no one at home,
before you put both feet on the floor
look in your loo and under your door.

And if you should see a bomb in your pan
run out of the door, escape while you can,
for you never know, it could happen to you -
you might be blown to pieces when sat on the loo!

Nappies Have Feelings Too!

Nappies have feelings
you know this is true,
they live and they breathe
just like me and you.

They need proper handling
they need special care,
each time that they're put
on a bottom that's bare.

It won't take a minute
to make sure it's well,
you could ask it its name
so it won't notice the smell

It won't take a second
to make it understand,
so be gentle with nappies,
take them by their hand!

For nappies have children
nappies like fun,
nappies can walk
and nappies can run.

Nappies can cry
and nappies are shy,
nappies can live
and nappies can die.

For nappies have feelings
you know this is true,
so be kind to your nappies
or they might empty on you

Chocolate Cake

My mother was an acrobat
my dad a clown,
they used to be famous
in every town.

Until, that is,
one Friday night
when a hungry-looking tiger
just fancied a bite.

He started to nibble
he began to roar,
he swallowed two toes
and then asked for more.

My dad, not knowing what
best he might do,
offered his trousers
and took off a shoe.

But a hungry-looking tiger
who's swallowed two toes
would be silly to stop now,
as he probably knows.

He crunched at a leg
he gobbled an ear,
swallowed an arm
and gurgled, 'Oh dear!'

Wiping his mouth
with a tiger-sized lick,
he spat out an arm
and was suddenly sick.

'Are you OK?'
my mum asked so lightly,
'Not really,' said the tiger,
swallowing politely.

'You see I think
I've made a terrible mistake,
toes are OK,
but I prefer chocolate cake!'

'Oh!' cried my mum
smiling at Dad.
'If it's chocolate cake that you want
there's no need to feel bad.'

And they turned to the table
where on it was found,
chocolate cakes piled high,
only two for a pound.

The tiger he gobbled
and gulped down the lot,
stopping only to say pardon
and why weren't they hot.

And with a whiskery grin,
a tiger-sized roar,
he sat down beside them
and then asked for more.

'Oh!' cried my mum.
'Ah!' said my dad,
you've eaten them all -
that's all that we had.

'We only keep them
as a bit of a treat,
come back tomorrow
or even next week!'

But tigers who've dined
and enjoyed a first course,
what they want now
is something with sauce.

A juicy second helping
to send cakes down a treat,
something much larger
and not quite so sweet.

He looked at my dad
and flicked out his tongue,
swallowed him whole
then looked at my mum.

A little more crunchy
with not so much taste,
but he gobbled her anyway,
leaving no waste!

Crocodile Frank

I had a crocodile
his name was Frank
he lived in our bath,
until he sank.
No one could find him,
not a sight,
until my sister went
for a scrub one night.

She dipped in a toe
then jumped in the tub,
she started to clean
she started to scrub,
but lurking about,
deep down below,
was a nasty crocodile,
as you probably know!

She reached for the soap
she stretched for the brush,
she knew, after all,
there was no great rush,
then sank into bubbles
and slipped under foam,
she closed both her eyes -
there was no one at home.

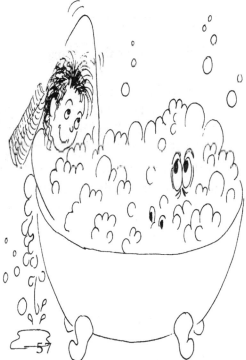

Suddenly there was a tickle on her foot
a nibble on her toe,
my sister she giggled
and shouted, 'Oh no!'
The crocodile sniffed
and in the wink of an eye
dreamed of eating small girls
in crocodile pie!

But remember that sisters
who giggle a lot
we should know that, once started,
they rarely can stop
for sniggering sisters,
as everyone knows,
like nothing better
than to tickle their toes!

She chuckled at the ceiling
and roared at the floor,
she opened her mouth
and shouted, 'No more!'
The crocodile, though hungry,
knew this not to be right
and so lifted his head
to take in this sight.

Of one giggling lady
aged only just nine,
no more than a mouthful
washed down with some wine,
of a girl not sent screaming
or running to the door
but who simply turns over
and chuckles, 'No more!'

This creature knew girls
if properly schooled,
know that crocodiles
never leave their food
and so there must be a lesson
or something been said
about young girls who giggle
and chuckle instead.

He scratched at his chin
and wiggled his ear,
he wiped from his eyes
a crocodile tear,
a tickle on his foot,
a nibble on his toe
he started to giggle
and shout, 'Oh no no!'

My sister she grins
and in the wink of an eye
dreams of sinking her teeth
into crocodile pie,
with a bottle of gravy
and buckets of chips -
grilled crocodile burgers
chopped into bits.

She opened her mouth
and for someone just nine
it was exceptionally large
and particularly fine,
with teeth that stuck out
as sharp as a spear
and a tongue that could kill
if you didn't keep clear.

She sank in her teeth
and tried for a bite,
to sample the flavour
and see what it's like
and, after a peck,
a bit of a nibble,
she slipped under water
to chew at its middle.

The crocodile gulped
with no wink in his eye
his mouth slid right shut
as he gurgled 'Oh my!'
for crocodiles, though wild,
it has to be said,
when bitten in their middle
are always soon dead.

Which is why my small sister
aged just under ten
can eat as much food
as ten hairy fat men
and probably why,
it has to be said,
we've never seen Grandad,
except for
his
HEAD!

Michael's Horrible Habits

Michael's horrible habits
always make the class feel ill,
for when it comes to nastiness
then we really have our fill.

For he can pull a face like Dracula's
and make his eyes turn red,
he can turn his tongue inside-out
so people think him dead.

He even collects old fingernails
and keeps them in a tin,
and has a set of old tissues
from the bottom of the bin.

He's rather good at flicking things
you'd never want to meet,
and you wouldn't believe the whiff
from his enormous dirty feet.

And if you should ever see
the gunge behind his ear,
this will be the moment
when you'll want to keep well clear

of Michael and his habits
of his horrid and nasty ways,
or you could find yourself
being sick for days and days.

Hopes and Feelings

(A serious poem)

First day at new school
children line up straight,
uniform without a crease,
graffiti by the gate.

Whispers on each corner
fingers pointing low,
booming voices mellow
to tell them where to go.

Corridors without bending
travel through the gloom,
polished floors lead the way
to another paint-chipped room.

Faces unfamiliar
turn the other way,
to hide for good the memories
and thoughts from their first day.

My Blister And Me

I've got a big blister
with a nice yellow head,
I suppose I could squeeze it
then watch it turn red.

I suppose I could squash it,
slowly at first,
just to see what it's like -
watching a big blister burst!

I suppose I could bite it
and swallow it whole,
I suppose I could pour it
into a bowl.

I suppose I could pick it
so it dribbles like goo,
I suppose I could eat it
in a big blister stew.

But I think I'll just wait
I think I'll just see,
just how well we get on -
my blister and me.

New Teacher

(A serious Poem)

New teacher in our school
couldn't control the fuss.

New teacher starting out,
not much older than us.

New teacher slams the door,
children start to cheer.

New teacher, gone for good,
happens every year.

Old teacher opens the door,
a lifetime older than us.

Old teacher, feet on table,
never controls the fuss.

Old teacher looks away,
his newspaper in the air.

New teacher tried her best,
old teacher doesn't care.

William Y-Front

William Y-Front could never go out
he could never play ball in the park,
for he'd been born in the shape of orange underpants
which glowed every night in the dark.

People would stop to catch just a glimpse,
they would wait at his house every day,
for a first look at William Y-Front
and that dazzling orange display.

Until poor William could take it no more
and so ran away right out to sea,
where he now has a job as a lighthouse
somewhere off the coast of Torquay.

How To Spot A Sister In Love

She spends even longer than usual in the bathroom
borrows Mum's old perfume
sits by the telephone all evening
keeps little notes under her pillow
giggles when you mention the boy's name
won't eat
changes her clothes every twenty minutes
keeps weighing herself
stays up late in the night playing mushy music
is early for school.

How To Spot A Brother In Love

He looks for hairs on his chin
starts missing football matches
buys aftershave
asks for his shirt to be ironed again - or does it himself!
asks his friends if he has spots
cuts his toenails
wants deodorant for his birthday
reads the problem pages in magazines
won't wear odd socks
cleans out his earwax
and is also early for school.

Mum's Gone Mad!

Mum's gone mad, Mum's gone crazy
she's planted tulips in the gravy.

Mum's gone daft, Mum's gone dippy,
she's dressed up as a hippy!

Mum's not right, Mum's not there
she's planted tulips in her hair.

Mum's gone goofy, Mum's gone mad
but wait until you spot our dad!

Dad's gone daft, he looks happy
with his bottle and that nappy!

Dad's gone bonkers, he's gone dotty
as he gurgles on his potty.

For there's one thing you cannot miss,
our mum and dad are round the twist!

King Henry VIII

King Henry was taught to hunt
he was taught to dance and sing,
he was taught to do all those things
expected of a king.

He was taught to give out orders
he was taught to plot and scheme
when all Henry really wanted
was to join a football team.

Which is why he wore big bloomers,
those which stuck out to the side,
so half a dozen football shorts
could be neatly tucked inside.

And why he always changed his wife
without looking for a reason,
except he thought it nice to have
a new wife for each season.

And, finally, why King Henry
liked to make heads roll -
just so he could have something
to kick into a goal!

Sid The Squid

Sid the squid
couldn't get rid
of his great big
goggly grin.

Other fish would hide
from that smile wide
at the bottom
of his wrinkly skin.

But what was worse,
a real curse,
what made him
like no other.

Is that his leer
from ear to ear
was shared by
his big brother.

And so, as a pair,
they would stop and stare
to make creatures
run for miles.

With their goggly grin
and wrinkly chin
and great big
ugly smiles.

The Victorian Sewer

The Victorian sewer
could smell of manure
and other things you just wouldn't sniff.

For, though very long,
it sometimes gave out a pong -
a terrible toe-turning whiff.

For this Victorian creation
although serving the nation
didn't do everything well.

For, although well intended
and often mended,
it gave off a terrible smell.

And the reason for this -
something you just couldn't miss
was that these sewers would suddenly stop.

Leaving their contents to travel
and quickly unravel
wherever they happened to drop!

Take A Seat

Way back in 1852
in a famous London street,
a gathering of young gentlemen
queued to take a seat.

But not so for the theatre,
not so for the Queen,
not so to see a show
or watch a football team.

No, all these young gentlemen
back in 1852,
queued to take a seat
on the first flushing public loo!

ENGAGED

Tots United

Tots United can't play football
they don't do as they're told
they're much too busy gurgling
for they're only two years old.

They're bottom in the league
they've never won the cup
and even when they try to run
their nappies won't stay up.

They like to play with potties
and throw dummies in the air,
but never try a tackle
in case they hurt their teddy bear.

For Tots United can't play football
they're no good on their feet,
until it comes to dribbling -
then Tots just can't be beat!

The Manure Cure

Let's hear it for horse muck,
it's a miracle cure!
Let's all go out
and mix with manure.

Let's all dive in
and sample the stink,
for manure is amazing
no matter what you think.

It can cure a cold
if squeezed up your nose,
it can make you run fast
if spread on your toes.

It can terrify tummy bugs
if swallowed quite quick,
for manure will never
make you feel sick.

So let's hear it for horse muck
let's enjoy the flavour,
for manure is really
something to savour!

Always Eat Your Earwax

Always eat your earwax
yes, that's what I said,
just pull it out in great big lumps
before you go to bed.

Then leave until the morning,
don't take a sneaky bite,
just wait for it to harden
as it turns to crusty white.

Then lick your lips and smile,
swallow it in one,
for you know that eating earwax
is always such great fun!

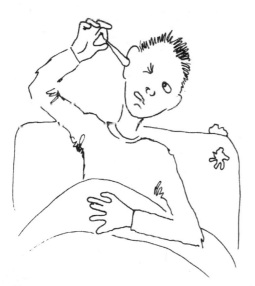

Your Teacher's Eyeball

The eyeball is waiting
it's watching you all,
it's blinking and twitching
from inside the school hall.

It's following your footsteps
it's there all the day,
it's one step behind
when you go out to play.

It knows if you're chewing
or can cheat in a test,
it glares and it stares
if you don't try your best.

It can roll in its socket
it can wriggle about,
and, if ever it's hungry,
the eyeball pops out.

That's when it's dangerous
when it wants to be fed,
that's when it turns
from deep blue to red.

That's when it's nasty
that's when it's cruel,
so always watch out
for your teacher's eyeball!

Cousin Colin

My cousin Colin
can sniff out a smell
from anywhere
in his street.

He can tell in a moment
if somebody near
has not changed the socks
on their feet.

He can capture the whiff
and pinpoint the pong
of rancid and rotten
roast beef.

He can sense the stink
of fingernail fluff
and bad breath
from mouldy old teeth.

Which is the reason
my cousin Colin
pulls faces
wherever he goes.

For he's been blessed
with what must be
the most enormous
super-sized nose!

BAD BREATH

SMELLY SOCKS

ROTTEN MEAT

With Thanks

To The King's England Press for having the courage to publish what is now a stream of best-selling books. In particular, thanks to Phil Rendell for putting a smile on all the faces of those wonderful people who sell books. Thanks too to Steve Rudd and Debbie Nunn for never doubting the potential of **Always Eat Your Bogies.**